The Worm Song and Other Tasty Tunes

The Worm Song

and Other Tasty Tunes

collected by **Janet Wilson**   illustrated by **Cory Wilson**

Scholastic Canada Ltd.

Scholastic Canada Ltd.
123 Newkirk Road, Richmond Hill, Ontario, Canada L4C 3G5

Scholastic Inc.
730 Broadway, New York, NY 10003, USA

Ashton Scholastic Pty Limited
PO Box 579, Gosford, NSW 2250, Australia

Ashton Scholastic Limited
Private Bag 1, Penrose, Auckland, New Zealand

Scholastic Publications Ltd.
Villiers House, Clarendon Avenue, Leamington Spa,
Warwickshire CV32 5PR, UK

Author's note:
The material for this book was collected orally from many sources. I have made an honest effort to ensure that the songs are in the public domain. If I have inadvertently infringed on any copyright, please accept my apology and forward the appropriate information to the Publisher.

Canadian Cataloguing in Publication Data

Main entry under title:

The Worm song and other tasty tunes

Without music
ISBN 0-590-74095-4

1. Children's songs – Texts. 2. Rhyming games.
I. Wilson, Janet, 1952– . II. Wilson, Cory, 1973– .

GR475.W67 1993   398.8   C93-093183-1

6 5 4 3 2 1   Printed in Canada   3 4 5 6 7/9

To my mother, Dorothy
my mother's sisters,
Margaret and Grace
and my sisters
Cathy and Diana

whose singing one afternoon
provided the inspiration for this book

Many thanks to all the friends and relatives who contributed their versions of songs and helped me track down that elusive verse. Especially helpful were my family; Diana, Shannon and Heather Reid; Cathy, Billy and Johnny Stacey; Vi, Arlene and Maureen Dunn; Barb deKat; Anne McKenna; Brenda Willis and Kassi Wilson; Maie Richards; and Mary Macdonald and her class.

Thanks to Yüksel Hassan and her art department for great work as usual and special thanks to Diane Kerner, senior editor, for her enthusiasm, great memory and particularly weird recollections!

Introduction

It began at a family gathering for my sister-in-law Rosemary's birthday. Three generations became embroiled in a heated discussion about the words to a childhood song.

I was struck at the time at how these songs have endured, evolving with society and remaining relevant to our culture. But mostly it was obvious to me how passionate we are about the songs of our childhood. I'm referring to "real kid" songs, the ones we sang on the bus or in the back seat of the station wagon, at camp and in the school yard.

Depending on where you live, you'll know different versions of some of these songs. Many of them, too, are the type that you make up as you go along. The fun in these is seeing how long you can keep coming up with new rhymes before driving someone nuts!

Because these songs are made up by kids, for kids, they deal with the topics that are most fascinating to children. There are those who will find the lyrics to some of these songs offensive. Adults, especially, bear the brunt of many of them. I hope they bear this with good humour. After all, adult disapproval has been a large reason for the enduring popularity of these "real kid" songs.

One last note: if you don't know the tunes for some of these, ask around. You're sure to know someone who does: a friend, a brother or sister, your dad . . . even grandma!

chapter 1

Eating worms

(not for the squeamish!)

MY STOMACH IS IN A COMMOTION

My stomach is in a commotion
I gotta lean over the rail
I don't want to dirty the ocean
Won't somebody please bring me a pail?

Come up, come up
Come up, dear supper, come up, come up
Come up, come up
Come up, dear supper, come up!

I'm a comin', I'm a comin'
Though my head is bending low
I hear the gentle voices calling,
"Hasten, Jason
Bring the basin
Whoops! Plop! Bring the mop!"

This song often naturally follows "The Worm Song." No wonder! Sing the first two verses to the tune of "My Bonnie Lies Over the Ocean" and sing the last verse to the tune of "Old Black Joe."

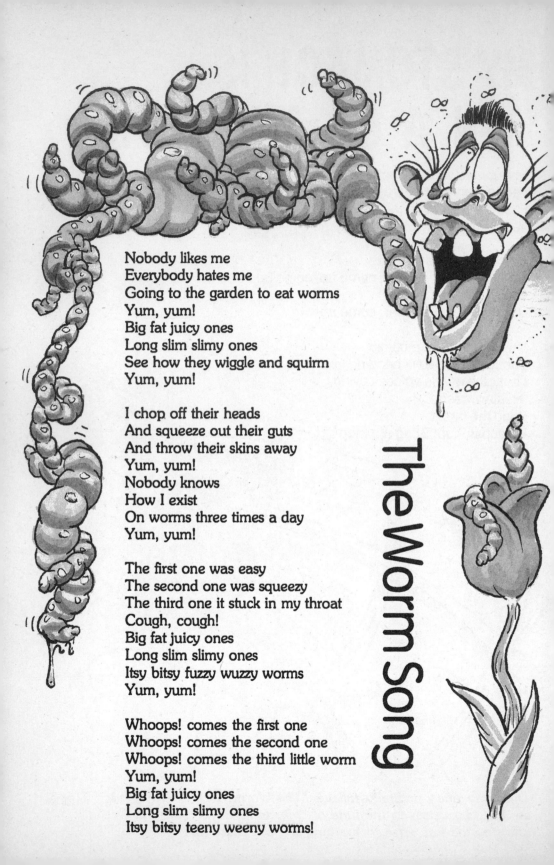

The Worm Song

Nobody likes me
Everybody hates me
Going to the garden to eat worms
Yum, yum!
Big fat juicy ones
Long slim slimy ones
See how they wiggle and squirm
Yum, yum!

I chop off their heads
And squeeze out their guts
And throw their skins away
Yum, yum!
Nobody knows
How I exist
On worms three times a day
Yum, yum!

The first one was easy
The second one was squeezy
The third one it stuck in my throat
Cough, cough!
Big fat juicy ones
Long slim slimy ones
Itsy bitsy fuzzy wuzzy worms
Yum, yum!

Whoops! comes the first one
Whoops! comes the second one
Whoops! comes the third little worm
Yum, yum!
Big fat juicy ones
Long slim slimy ones
Itsy bitsy teeny weeny worms!

A Little Birdie in The Sky

A little birdie in the sky
Dropped some white stuff in my eye
I didn't weep
I didn't cry
I'm just glad that cows don't fly!

The Skunk Hole

Oh-h-h-h-h
I stuck my head in the little skunk's hole
And the little skunk said,
"Well, bless my soul
Take it out
Take it out
Take it out
Remove it!"

Oh-h-h-h-h
I didn't take it out
And the little skunk said,
"If you don't take it out
You'll wish you had!
Take it out
Take it out!"

Pee-hew!
I removed it!

Sing to the tune of "Dixie."

HOW DRY I AM

How dry I am
How wet I'll be
If I don't find
The bathroom key.

It's too late now
It's on the floor
My rubber girdle
Won't hold no more.

Replace the words of the traditional tune, "How Dry I Am," with these ones.

Baby Bumblebee

I'm bringing home a baby bumblebee
Won't my mommy be so proud of me
I'm bringing home a baby bumblebee
Ooh-ee!
It's stinging me!

I'm squishing up my baby bumblebee
Won't my mommy be so proud of me
I'm squishing up my baby bumblebee
Ooh-ee!
It's all over me!

I'm licking up my baby bumblebee
Won't my mommy be so proud of me
I'm licking up my baby bumblebee
Ooh-ee!
The bee's in me!

I'm bringing up my baby bumblebee
Won't my mommy be so proud of me
I'm bringing up my baby bumblebee
Ooh-ee!
There's the mommy bee!

Sing to the tune of "The Arkansas Traveller."

I'm bringing home a baby bumblebee
Won't my mommy be so proud of me
I'm bringing home a baby bumblebee
Ooh-eeh!
It's stinging me!

I'm bringing home a baby dinosaur
Won't my mommy hide behind the door
I'm bringing home a baby dinosaur
Ooh oohl
He messed on the floor!

I'm bringing home a baby puddy-tat
Won't my doggy be so glad of that
I'm bringing home a baby puddy-tat
Mee-ow!
See her scat!

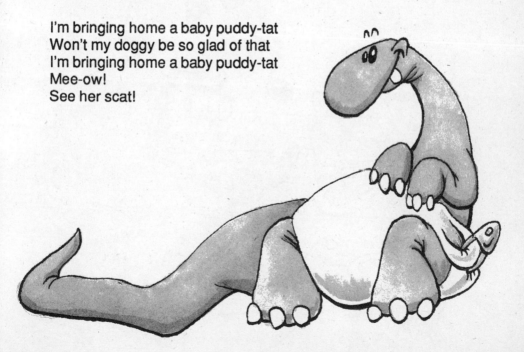

Beans, Beans

Beans, beans, the musical fruit
The more you eat, the more you toot!
The more you toot, the better you feel
So eat beans, beans for every meal.

Great Green Gobs

Great green gobs of
Greasy grimy gopher guts
Mutilated monkey meat
Dirty little birdies' feet
Top it all off with petrified pelican puke
And I forgot my spoon!
(But I brought a straw. . . .)

Sing to the tune of "The Old Grey Mare."

Black Socks

Black socks, they never get dirty
The longer you wear them, the stronger they get
Sometimes I think I should launder them
Something keeps telling me
"Don't wash them yet, not yet, not yet, not yet . . . "

Sing as a round.

Dirty Lil

Dirty Lil, Dirty Lil
Lives up on garbage hill
Never washes, never will
Hoo-ee!
Dirty Lil!

Dirty Pete, Dirty Pete
Always smells like rotten meat
Cannot stand to wash his feet
Hoo-ee!
Dirty Pete!

Dirty Tess, Dirty Tess
Never washed a single tress
Her hair was such a total mess
Hoo-ee!
Dirty Tess!

Dirty Luke, Dirty Luke
Never showered, the filthy kook
Stunk so bad it made you puke
Hoo-ee!
Dirty Luke!

Have fun making up your own verses with the names of friends! Sing this one to the tune of "The Little Brown Jug."

UNDERWEAR

I have lost my underwear
I don't care, I'll go bare
Bye-bye, longjohns.

They were very near to me
Tickled me — hee, hee, hee!
Bye-bye, longjohns.

How I miss that trap door behind me
If I'm lost you'll know where to find me
I have lost my underwear
I'll go bare
I don't care
Longjohns, bye-bye!

Sing to the tune of "Bye-Bye, Blackbird."

pOpeye

I'm Popeye, the sailor man
I live in a garbage can
I eat all the worms
And spit out the germs
I'm Popeye, the sailor man.

I'm Popeye, the sailor man
I live in a frying pan
I love to go swimmin'
With all kinds of women
I'm Popeye, the sailor man!
Toot! Toot!

chapter 2

ACORN BROWN
AND OTHER NUTS

Acorn Brown

I'm a little acorn brown
Lying on the cold, cold ground
Everybody steps on me
That is why I'm cracked you see.

CHORUS:
I'm a nut, *click click*
In a rut, *click click*
I'm a nut, *click click*
In a rut, *click click.*

I love me, I think I'm grand
I sit in the movies and hold my hand
I put my arm around my waist
When I get fresh, I slap my face.

(CHORUS)

I call myself on the telephone
Just to see if I am home
I ask myself out for a date
And pick myself up at half past eight.

(CHORUS)

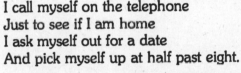

Have fun making the clicking sound in the refrain by sucking one side of your teeth.

Ping-pong Ball

Paul's got a head like a ping-pong ball
Paul's got a head like a ping-pong ball
Paul's got a head like a ping-pong ball
Ping! Like a ping-pong ball.

Ping-pong, ping-pong, ping-pong
Ping-pong, ping-pong, ping-pong, ping-pong ball
Ping-pong, ping-pong, ping-pong
Ping-pong, ping-pong, ping-pong, ping-pong ball!

Paul's got a head like a pong-ping ball
Paul's got a head like a pong-ping ball
Paul's got a head like a pong-ping ball
Pong! Like a pong-ping ball.

Pong-ping, pong-ping, pong-ping
Pong-ping, pong-ping, pong-ping, pong-ping ball
Pong-ping, pong-ping, pong-ping
Pong-ping, pong-ping, pong-ping, pong-ping ball!

This tongue-twister is sung to the tune of "The William Tell Overture."

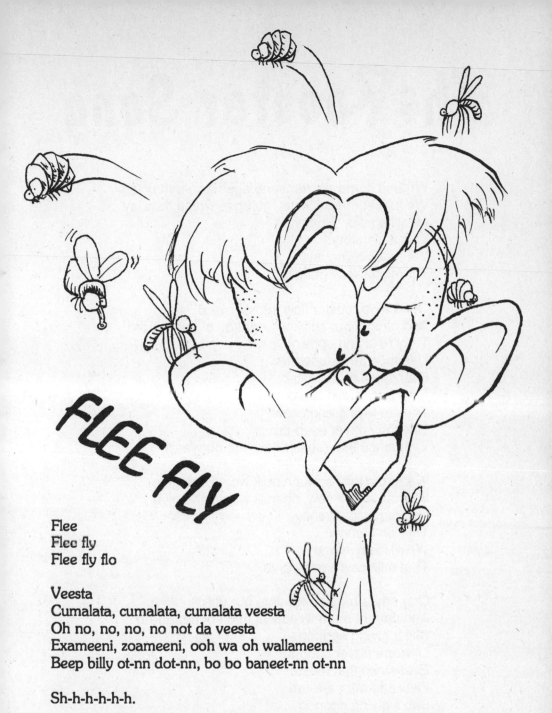

FLEE FLY

Flee
Flee fly
Flee fly flo

Veesta
Cumalata, cumalata, cumalata veesta
Oh no, no, no, no not da veesta
Exameeni, zoameeni, ooh wa oh wallameeni
Beep billy ot-nn dot-nn, bo bo baneet-nn ot-nn

Sh-h-h-h-h.

This a rote song for two groups. After the first group sings the first line of lyrics, the other group repeats them. Then the first group sings the next line, the other group repeats them, and so on. The groups sing the last line, "Sh-h-h-h-h," all together.

The Rooster Song

We had some chickens, no eggs would they lay
We had some chickens, no eggs would they lay
My wife said, "Honey,
This isn't funny.
We're losin' money.
Them chickens gotta lay!"

One day a rooster flew into our yard
And caught our chickens right off of their guard
They're laying eggs now
Like they never used-ter
Ever since that rooster
Flew into our ya-a-ard
They're laying eggs now
Like they never used-ter
Ever since that rooster flew into our yard!

We had a milk cow, no milk would she give
We had a milk cow, no milk would she give
My wife said, "Honey,
This isn't funny.
We're losin' money.
That milk cow's gotta give."

One day a rooster flew into our yard
And caught our milk cow right off of her guard
She's giving eggnog
Like she never used-ter
Ever since that rooster
Flew into our ya-a-ard
She's giving eggnog
Like she never used-ter
Ever since that rooster flew into our yard!

We had a gum tree, no gum would she give
We had a gum tree, no gum would she give
My wife said, "Honey,
This isn't funny.
We're losing money.
That gum tree's gotta give."

One day a rooster flew into our yard
And caught our gum tree right off of its guard
It's giving Chiclets
Like it never used-ter
Ever since that rooster
Flew into our ya-a-ard
It's giving Chiclets
Like it never used-ter
Ever since that rooster flew into our yard!

I Like To Eat

I like to eat
I like to eat
I like to eat
Eat apples and bananas
(repeat entire verse.)

Ay lake tay ate
Ay lake tay ate
Ay lake tay ate
Ate ay-ples and bay-nay-nays
(repeat).

Ee leek tee eat
Ee leek tee eat
Ee leek tee eat
Eat ee-ples and bee-nee-nees
(repeat).

I like tie ite
I like tie ite
I like tie ite
Ite ei-ples and bie-nie-nies
(repeat).

You'll notice that each verse following the first verse replaces all the vowels in the song (except the "and") with a single vowel. Start with the first vowel in the alphabet and continue the next verse with the next one, and so on.

One Bottle of Pop

One bottle of pop
Two bottle of pop
Three bottle of pop
Four bottle of pop
Five bottle of pop
Six bottle of pop
Seven seven bottle of pop.

Fish and chips and vinegar
Vinegar, vinegar
Fish and chips and vinegar
Pepper, pepper, pepper, salt.

Don't throw your trash in my back yard
My back yard, my backyard
Don't throw your trash in my back yard
My back yard's full!

This one is fun to sing as a round!

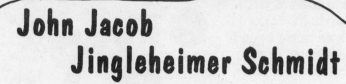

John Jacob
Jingleheimer Schmidt

John Jacob Jingleheimer Schmidt
That's my name too
Whenever we go out
The people always shout
John Jacob Jingleheimer Schmidt!
La, la, la, la, la, la, la . . .

For this one, sing the words loudly and the "la, la," part softly. Then repeat the song three or four times, each time singing the words more softly and the "la, la, la," louder.

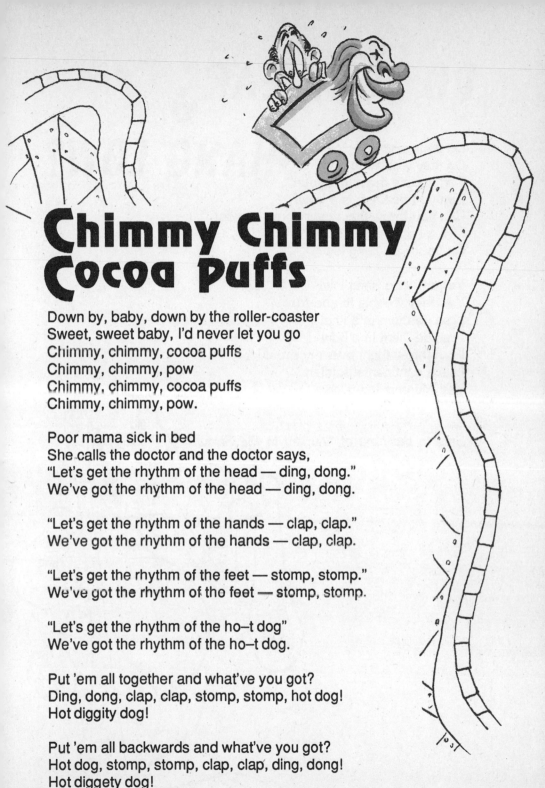

Chimmy Chimmy Cocoa Puffs

Down by, baby, down by the roller-coaster
Sweet, sweet baby, I'd never let you go
Chimmy, chimmy, cocoa puffs
Chimmy, chimmy, pow
Chimmy, chimmy, cocoa puffs
Chimmy, chimmy, pow.

Poor mama sick in bed
She calls the doctor and the doctor says,
"Let's get the rhythm of the head — ding, dong."
We've got the rhythm of the head — ding, dong.

"Let's get the rhythm of the hands — clap, clap."
We've got the rhythm of the hands — clap, clap.

"Let's get the rhythm of the feet — stomp, stomp."
We've got the rhythm of the feet — stomp, stomp.

"Let's get the rhythm of the ho–t dog"
We've got the rhythm of the ho–t dog.

Put 'em all together and what've you got?
Ding, dong, clap, clap, stomp, stomp, hot dog!
Hot diggity dog!

Put 'em all backwards and what've you got?
Hot dog, stomp, stomp, clap, clap, ding, dong!
Hot diggety dog!

This is an action chant. Make up actions for each rhythm!

DO YOUR EARS HANG LOW?

Do your ears hang low
Do they wobble to and fro?
Can you tie them in a knot?
Can you tie them in a bow?
Can you throw them over your shoulder
Like a continental soldier?
Do your ears hang low?

Yes, my ears hang low
Yes, they wobble to and fro
I can tie them in a knot
I can tie them in a bow
I can throw them over my shoulder
Like a continental soldier
Yes! My ears hang low!

Sing to the tune of "Turkey in the Straw."

I See London, I See France

I see London
I see France
I see Chris's underpants
Not too big
Not too small
Just the size of Montreal.

Feel free to replace the name in the third line with any name of your choice!

In The Land of OZ

In the land of Oz
Where the ladies smoke cigars
Every puff they take
Is enough to kill a snake.

When the snakes are dead
They put roses in their head
When the roses die
They put diamonds in their eyes
When the diamonds break
Then it's 1998.

POOR LITTLE bug

Poor little bug on the wall
No one to love him at all
No one to wash his clothes
No one to tickle his toes
No one to love him at all.

Poor little fly on the wall
He ain't got no clothes on at all
No shimmy, no shirtie
No pantie, no skirtie
The poor little fly on the wall!

Repeat the lyrics to this song over and over, singing them with a different style each time. For example, sing them happily, sadly, operatically, even babyishly!

THE PRUNE SONG

No matter how young a prune may be
He's always full of wrinkles
A baby prune is like his dad
But he's not wrinkled quite as bad.

We have wrinkles on our face
A prune has wrinkles every place
No matter how young a prune may be
He's always full of wrinkles!

BOOM BOOM

CHORUS:
Boom, boom, ain't it great to be crazy?
Boom, boom, ain't it great to be crazy?
Giddy and foolish the whole day long
Boom, boom, ain't it great to be crazy?

Eli, Eli, he sells socks
Ten cents a pair and a dollar a box
The longer you wear them, the stronger they get
Put 'em in the water and they don't get wet!
(CHORUS)

A man bought a pair of combination underwear
Wore 'em nine months without a single tear
Wore 'em nine months without a saturation
Couldn't get them off 'cause he lost tho combination!
(CHORUS)

A horse and a flea and three blind mice
Sat on a curbstone shooting dice
The horse, he slipped and fell on his knee
"Whoops," said the flea, "There's a horsey on me!"
(CHORUS)

Way down south where the bananas grow
A grasshopper stepped on an elephant's toe
The elephant said, with tears in his eyes,
"Why don't you pick on someone your own size?"
(CHORUS)

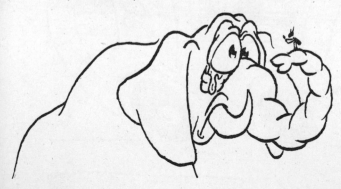

Here Comes My WAGON

Ding, ding, ding, ding, ding
Here comes my wagon
To take me to the nutty factory
Ding, ding, ding, ding, ding
Here comes my wagon
Can't you hear my keeper calling me?

Just like the nuts that fall
I'm a little cracked that's all
Ding, ding, ding, ding, ding
Here comes my wagon
My kiddie car, my train
Woooo! Woooo!

OLD MRS. PRISS

Old Mrs. Priss
Went out to pi—ck some flowers
And in the grass
She wet her a—nkles to her knees
And in the coop
She let a poo—r old chicken die
And in the cart
She let a far—mer pass her by.

And there was Granny
Swinging on the outhouse door
(In just her nightie)
Waiting for the garbage man
(Who was a playboy)
Brother could you ask for more!

Miss Lucy Had A Baby

Miss Lucy had a baby
She called him Tiny Tim
She put him in the bathtub
To see if he could swim
He drank up all the water
He ate up all the soap
He tried to eat the bathtub
But it wouldn't go down his throat.

Miss Lucy called a doctor
The doctor called a nurse
The nurse called the lady
With the alligator purse
"Measles!" said the doctor
"Mumps!" said the nurse
"Goosebumps!" said the lady
With the alligator purse.

"Pills!" said the doctor
"Penicillin!" said the nurse
"Pizza!" said the lady
With the alligator purse.

Out walked the doctor
Out walked the nurse
Out walked the lady
With Tim in her purse.

I WENT TO THE CORNER RESTAURANT

CHORUS :
I went to the corner restaurant
To buy a loaf of bread bread bread
They wrapped it up in bubble gum
And this is what they said said said:

My name is Elvis Presley
Girls are sexy
Sittin' in the backseat
Drinkin' Pepsi
Push-up!

(CHORUS)

My name is P–I–Pickle–I
Pickle–I–Kay
I run around berries
All over cherries
Chinese chopsticks
Do me a favour
Do you like ice cream?
Push-ups!

chapter 3

THE HEARSE SONG

THE HEARSE SONG

Don't ever laugh when the hearse goes by
Or you may be the next to die
Ah-ooo! Ah-ooo!

They'll wrap you up in a clean white sheet
And put you down about six feet deep
Ah-ooo! Ah-ooo!

And all goes well for about a week
And then your coffin begins to leak
Ah-ooo! Ah-ooo!

The worms crawl in, the worms crawl out
The worms play pinochle on your snout
Ah-ooo! Ah-ooo!

They eat your eyes, they eat your nose
They eat the jelly between your toes
Ah-ooo! Ah-ooo!

They eat your clothes, they eat your hat
They crawl in skinny, then they crawl out fat
Ah-ooo! Ah-ooo!

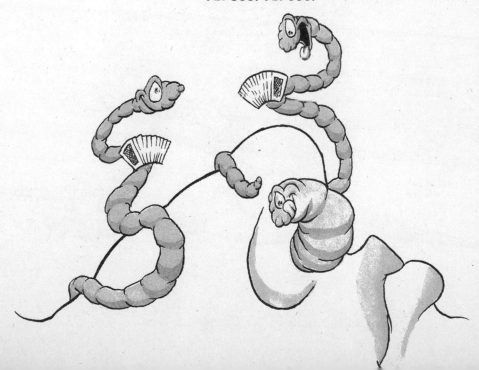

TOM THE TOAD

Oh, Tom the toad
Oh, Tom the toad
Why are you lying on the road?
Oh, Tom the toad
Oh, Tom the toad
Why are you lying on the road?
You didn't see the car ahead
Now you're all marked with tire tread.
Oh, Tom the toad
Oh, Tom the toad
Why are you lying on the road?

Sing to the tune of "O Christmas Tree."

He Jumped from Twenty Thousand Feet

He jumped from twenty thousand feet
Without a parachute
He jumped from twenty thousand feet
WIthout a parachute
He jumped from twenty thousand feet
Without a parachute
And he'll never jump again!

CHORUS:
Glory, glory, what a heckuva way to die
Glory, glory, what a heckuva way to die
Glory, glory, what a heckuva way to die
And he'll never jump again!

Sing to the tune of "The Battle Hymn of the Republic."

The Boa Constrictor

I'm being eaten by a boa constrictor
Boa constrictor, boa constrictor
I'm being eaten by a boa constrictor
And I don't like it a bit!

Oh, no! He's got me toe
Oh, gee! He's up to me knee
Oh, dear! He's reached me rear
Oh, fiddle! He's squeezing me middle
Oh, heck! He's up to me neck
Oh, dread! He's right to me head
O, drat! He's at me hat . . .

HELP!

THE WATERMELON SONG

You can plant a watermelon up above my grave
And let the juice — *SLURP!* — seep through
You can plant a watermelon up above my grave
That's all I ask of you.

Well, some folks say that steak is fine
But I prefer a watermelon rind
You can plant a watermelon up above my grave
And let the juice — *SLURP!* — through.

Instead of saying the word "slurp," make a slurping sound. You can replace the word "steak" with the name of any food. How about your favourite snack?

Peanut Butter

A peanut sat on a railway track
His heart was all aflutter
Around the corner
Came a railroad train
CHOO! CHOO!
Peanut butter!

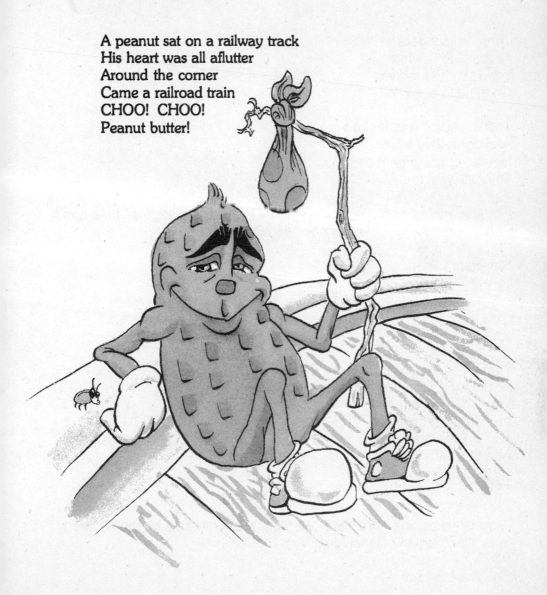

Three Little Angels

1:

Three little angels
All dressed in white
Tried to get to heaven
On the end of a kite.

The kite string was broken
And down they all fell
Instead of going to heaven
They all went to . . .

(Repeat, replacing "three little angels" with "two little angels," then again
with "one little angel." Then conclude with . . .)

She went to bed!

2:

Three little Martians
All dressed in green
Tried to get to heaven
In a washing machine
The washer was broken
And down they all fell
Instead of going to heaven
They all went to . . .

(Repeat, replacing "three little Martians" with "two little Martians," then
"one little Martian." Conclude with . . .)

She went to bed!

3:

Three little devils
All dressed in red
Tried to get to heaven
On the end of a bed
The bed post was broken
And down they all fell
Instead of going to heaven
They all went to . . .

(Repeat, replacing "three little devils" with "two little devils," then again
with "one little devil." Then conclude with . . .)

He went to bed!

OOOEY GOOEY

Ooey Gooey was a worm
A silly worm was he
He played upon a railway track
A train he did not see . . .

OOOEY! GOOEY!

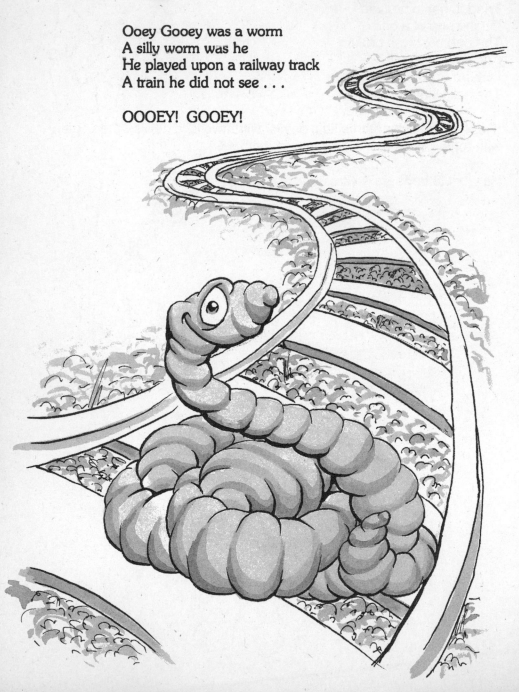

Miss Mary Mack

Miss Mary Mack, Mack, Mack
All dressed in black, black, black
With silver buttons, buttons, buttons
All down her back, back, back.

She doesn't read, read, read
She doesn't write, write, write
She only smokes, smokes, smokes
Her father's pipe, pipe, pipe.

She asked her mother, mother, mother
For fifty cents, cents, cents
To watch the elephant, elephant, elephant
Jump over the fence, fence, fence.

He jumped so high, high, high
He reached the sky, sky, sky
And didn't come back, back, back
Until July, July, July.

She went upstairs, upstairs, upstairs
To say her prayers, prayers, prayers
She bumped her head, head, head
And now she's dead, dead, dead!

This is a popular clapping song with a staccato rhythm.

Alice Where Are You Going?

Alice, where are you going?
"Upstairs to take a bath."
Alice, with the legs like toothpicks
And a neck like a giraffey — raffy, raffy, raffy

Alice, what are you doing?
Alice! Don't pull that plug!
Oh my goodness, oh my soul
There goes Alice down the hole!

Alice, what are you saying?
"Bubble, bubble, bubble, bubble . . ."

MAGALENA HAGALENA

CHORUS:
Magalena Hagalena
Ookahtahka Wahkahtahka
Oka Moka Poka was her name.

She had two eyes
In the middle of her head
One was green
And the other was red.
(CHORUS)

She had two teeth
In the middle of her mouth
One pointed north
And the other pointed south.
(CHORUS)

She had five hairs
In the top of her head
Three were alive
And two were dead.
(CHORUS)

She had two feet
Like bathroom mats
Don't ask me
How they got like that.
(CHORUS)

A ten-ton truck
Hit poor Magalena
The poor truck driver
Had to buy a new machine-a
(CHORUS)

chapter 4

Ninety-Nine Bottles of Beer and Other Classics

Ninety-Nine Bottles of Beer
Helen Had a Steamboat
The Ship Titanic
Gee, Ma!
The Quartermaster's Store
Oh, Chester
Down by the Bay
Hey Lawdy Lo
When Billy Was One
Found a Peanut
There's a Hole in My Bucket
Alice the Camel
I Had a Little Chicken
The Other Day
Kookaburra
Fuzzy Wuzzy
A Sailor Went To Sea

Ninety-Nine Bottles

Ninety-nine bottles of beer on the wall,
Ninety-nine bottles of beer
If one of these bottles should happen to fall
Ninety-eight bottles of beer on the wall.

Ninety-eight bottles of beer on the wall
Ninety-eight bottles of beer
If one of these bottles should happen to fall
Ninety-seven bottles of beer on the wall.

(Repeat the song, descending numerically, until . . .)

One bottle of beer on the wall
One bottle of beer
If this bottle should happen to fall . . .

Ninety-nine bottles of beer on the wall!

This one can go on forever, and it's guaranteed to drive people nuts on a long car drive.

Helen Had A Steamboat

Helen had a steamboat
Her steamboat had a bell
When Helen went to heaven
Her steamboat went to . . .

Hello operator
Please give me number nine
And if you disconnect me
I'll kick you up . . .

Behind the Iron Curtain
There was a piece of glass
When Helen sat upon it
She hurt her little . . .

Ask me no more questions
I'll tell you no more lies
The boys are in the bathroom
Pulling down their . . .

Flies are in the garbage
Bees are in the park
Boys and girls are kissing
In the dark, dark, dark!

The ship, *Titanic*

Oh, they built the ship, *Titanic*
To sail the ocean blue
And they thought they had a ship
That the ocean would not come through
But the Good Lord raised His hand
Said the ship would never land
It was sad when the great ship went down.

CHORUS:
Oh, it was sad
so sad
it was sad
too bad
It was sad when the great ship went down
To the bottom of the sea
Husbands and wives, little children lost their lives
It was sad when the great ship went down.

Oh, they were not far from shore
When they heard a mighty roar
And the rich refused to
Associate with the poor
So they put them down below
Where they'd be the first to go
It was sad when the great ship went down.

(CHORUS)

Oh, the *Californ-i-a*,
Not a dozen miles away
Never heard their SOS
'Cause the crew had hit the hay
So the captain and the crew
Never knew the ship was through
It was sad when the great ship went down.

(CHORUS)

Oh, they put the lifeboats out
On that dark and stormy sea
While the band struck up
"Nearer my God to Thee"
Oh, husbands and wives,
Little children lost their lives
It was sad when tho great ship went down.

(CHORUS)

Oh, the moral of this story
Is very plain to see
Always bring a rubber ducky
In case of emergency
For uncles and aunts,
Little children lost their pants
It was sad when the great ship went down
Kerplunk! It sunk!
What a hunk of junk!

Gee, Ma!

They say that in the Army
The food is mighty fine
A bun rolled off the table
And killed a pal of mine.

CHORUS:
Oh, I don't want no more of Army life
Gee, Ma! I wanna go
But they won't let me go
Gee, Ma! I wanna go home!

They say that in the Army
The drinks are mighty fine
You ask for Coca-Cola
They give you turpentine.

(CHORUS)

They say that in the Army
The boys are mighty fine
You ask for Kevin Costner
They give you Frankenstein!

(CHORUS)

*Here's another song you can make up endless
verses to.*

The Quartermaster's Store

CHORUS:
My eyes are dim, I cannot see
I have not brought my specs with me
I have not brought my specs with me.

There were beans, beans big as submarines
In the store, in the store
There were beans, beans big as submarines
In the Quartermaster's store
(CHORUS)

There were deers, deers wearing pink brassieres
In the store, in the store
There were deers, deers wearing pink brassieres
In the Quartermaster's store
(CHORUS)

There were bananas, bananas wearing striped pajamas
In the store, in the store
There were bananas, bananas wearing striped pajamas
In the Quartermaster's store.
(CHORUS)

This is a great song to make up your own lyrics to — try using your friends' names!

Oh, Chester

Oh, Chester	(touch your chest)
Have you heard	(pull your ear lobe)
About Harry?	(put your hand on your head)
Just	(touch your chest)
Got back	(touch your back)
From the arm-y	(touch your arm, then point to yourself)
I	(touch your eye)
Hear	(pull your ear lobe)
He knows	(touch your nose)
How to wear a rose	(make a circle on your chest with your finger)
Hip	(touch one of your hips)
Hip	(touch your other hip)
Hoo-ray	(throw both of your arms in the air)
For the arm-y!	(touch your arm, then point to yourself)

Sing this song faster each time you repeat it. Stand up each time you sing the word "rose." It makes it easier to really give your hips a good slap!

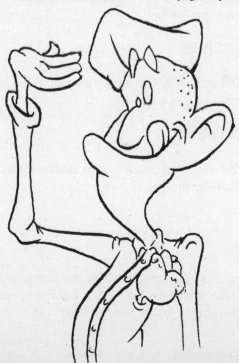

Down By The Bay

CHORUS:
Down by the bay
Down by the bay
Where the watermelons grow
Where the watermelons grow
Back to my home
Back to my home
I dare not go
I dare not go
For if I do
For if I do
My mother will say:
My mother will say:

"Did you ever see a fly with a polka dot tie
Down by the bay?"

(CHORUS)

"Did you ever see a pig wearing a wig
Down by the bay?"

(CHORUS)

"Did you ever see a bear combing his hair
Down by the bay?"

(CHORUS)

"Did you ever see a goose kissing a moose
Down by the bay?"

This is a fun rote song. Half the group sings the song, and the other half repeats each line (the words in the italics below) as an echo. Each person can take a turn making up a wacky question that "mother will say"!

Hey Lawdy Lo

CHORUS:
Hey lawdy, lawdy, lawdy
Hey lawdy, lawdy, lo
Hey lawdy, lawdy, lawdy
Hey lawdy, lawdy, lo.

I know a girl her name is Heather
Hey lawdy, lawdy, lo
She sings songs in all kinds of weather
Hew lawdy, lawdy, lo.

(CHORUS)

I know a boy whose name is Billy
Hey lawdy, lawdy, lo
He tells jokes that are really silly
Hey lawdy, lawdy, lo.

(CHORUS)

Make up verses to this song using the names of your friends and family members.

When Billy Was One

When my Billy was one
He learned to suck his thumb
Thumb, Billy, thumb, Billy
Half past one.

And when my Billy was two
He learned to tie his shoe
Shoe, Billy, shoe, Billy
Half past two.

And when my Billy was three
He learned to climb a tree
Tree, Billy, tree, Billy
Half past three

(Sing the following verses in the same pattern:)

And when my Billy was four
He finally reached the door . . .

And when my Billy was five
He learned to swim and dive . . .

And when my Billy was six
He learned to pick up sticks . . .

And when my Billy was seven
He could count to seven . . .

And when my Billy was eight
He learned to roller-skate . . .

And when my Billy was nine
He learned to sing so fine . . .

And when my Billy was ten
He learned to say "the end!"

Found A Peanut

Found a peanut
Found a peanut
Found a peanut last night
Last night I found a peanut
Found a peanut last night

Broke it open
Broke it open
Broke it open last night
Last night I broke it open
Broke it open last night

It was rotten
It was rotten
It was rotten last night
Last night it was rotten
It was rotten last night.

(Sing the following verses by continuing to follow the lyric pattern:)

Ate it anyway . . .

Got a tummyache . . .

Called a doctor . . .

Appendicitis . . .

Operation . . .

Died anyway . . .

Went to heaven . . .

Didn't want me . . .

Went the other way . . .

(And finish up with:)
It was a dream
All a dream
It was a dream last night
Last night it was a dream
It was a dream last night.

Sing to the tune of "My Darling Clementine."

THERE'S A HOLE IN MY BUCKET

(HENRY:)

There's a hole in my bucket, dear Liza, dear Liza
There's a hole in my bucket, dear Liza, a hole

(LIZA:)

Then fix it, dear Henry, dear Henry, dear Henry
Then fix it dear Henry, dear Henry, fix it

(HENRY:)

With what shall I fix it, dear Liza, dear Liza?
With what shall I fix it, dear Liza? With what?

(LIZA:)

With a straw, dear Henry, dear Henry, dear Henry
With a straw, dear Henry, dear Henry, a straw

(Sing the following verses by continuing to follow
the lyric pattern:)

(HENRY:)	(LIZA:)
The straw is too long ...	*Then cut it ...*
With what shall I cut it ... ?	*With a knife ...*
The knife is too blunt ...	*Then sharpen it ...*
With what shall I sharpen it ...?	*With a stone ...*
The stone is too dry ...	*Then wet it ...*

With what shall I wet it . . . ? *With water . . .*

In what shall I get it . . . *In a bucket . . .*

But there's a hole in my bucket , dear Liza, dear Liza . . .

Alice The Camel

Alice the camel has ten humps
Alice the camel has ten humps
Alice the camel has ten humps
So go, Alice, go
Boom, Boom, Boom

Alice the camel has nine humps
Alice the camel has nine humps
Alice the camel has nine humps
So go, Alice, go
Boom, Boom, Boom

Alice the camel has eight humps
Alice the camel has eight humps
Alice the camel has eight humps
So go, Alice, go
Boom, Boom, Boom

(Repeat, giving Alice fewer and fewer humps, until . . .)

Alice the camel has no humps
Alice the camel has no humps
Alice the camel has no humps
'Cause Alice is a horse, of course!

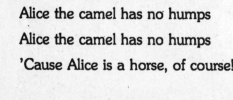

Sing to the tune of "Them Bones"

I HAD A LITTLE CHICKEN

I had a little chicken
And it wouldn't lay an egg
So I poured hot water
Up and down its leg.

The little chicken cried
And the little chicken begged
And the poor little chicken
Laid a hard-boiled egg.

I had a little chicken
And it wouldn't lay an egg
So I poured hot chocolate
Up and down its leg.

The little chicken cried
And the little chicken begged
And the poor little chicken
Laid an Easter egg.

I had a little chicken
And it wouldn't lay an egg
So I poured a school bus
Up and down its leg.

The little chicken cried
And the little chicken begged
And the poor little chicken
Laid a hand grenade.

The Other Day

The other day
I met a bear
A great big bear
Away up there
The other day I met a bear
I met a bear away up there.

He looked at me
I looked at him
He smiled at me
I smiled at him
He looked at me, I looked at him
He smiled at me, I smiled at him.

He said to me
"You 'd better run
For I can see
You 've got no gun"
He said to me, "You'd better run
For I can see you've got no gun."

And so I ran
Away from there
And right behind
Me ran that bear
And so I ran away from there
And right behind me ran that bear.

In front of me
There was a tree
The biggest tree
You ever did see.
In front of me there was a tree
The biggest tree you ever did see.

And so I jumped
Into the air
But I missed the branch
On the way up there
And so I jumped into the air
But I missed the branch on the way up there.

Now don't you fret
Now don't you frown
'Cause I caught that branch
On the way back down!
Now don't you fret, now don't you frown
'Cause I caught that branch on the way back down!

This is the end
There ain't no more
Unless I meet
That bear once more
This is the end, there ain't no more
Unless I meet that bear once more.

And so I met
That bear once more
Now he's a rug
On the living room floor
And so I met that bear once more
Now he's a bear on the living room floor!

This is another rote song — one person sings a line and the rest of the group repeats it. Everyone sings the last two lines of the verse together.

KOOKABURRA

Kookaburra sits in the old gum tree
Merry, merry king of the bush is he
Laugh, kookaburra, laugh, kookaburra
Gay your life must be
Ha! ha! ha!

Kookaburra sits in the old gum tree
Counting all the monkeys he can see
Stop, kookaburra, stop, kookaburra
That's not a monkey
That's me!
Ha! ha! ha!

Kookaburra sits in the old gum tree
Eating all the gum drops he can see
Stop, kookaburra, stop, kookaburra
Please save some for me
Ha! ha! ha!

Kookaburra sits on the electric wire
Tears in his eyes and his pants on fire
Ouch, kookaburra, ouch, kookaburra
Hot your tail must be
Ow! ow! ow!

Fuzzy Wuzzy

Fuzzy Wuzzy was a bear
Fuzzy Wuzzy had no hair
Fuzzy Wuzzy wasn't fuzzy
Was he?

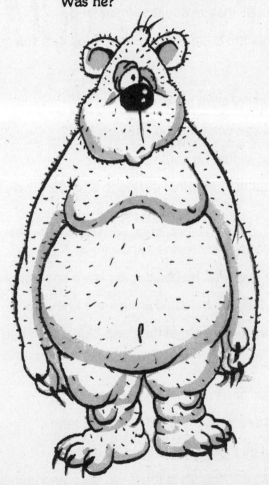

A SAILOR WENT TO SEA

A sailor went to sea sea sea

To see what he could see see see

But all that he could see see see

Was the bottom of the deep blue sea sea sea!

A sailor went to diz diz diz

To see what he could diz diz diz

But all that he could diz diz diz

Was the bottom of the deep blue diz diz diz!

A sailor went to knee knee knee

To see what he could knee knee knee

But all that he could knee knee knee

Was the bottom of the deep blue knee knee knee!

A sailor went to land land land

To see what he could land land land

But all that he could land land land

Was the bottom of the deep blue land land land!

A sailor went to diz knee land

To see what he could diz knee land

But all that he could diz knee land

Was the bottom of the deep blue

Disneyland!

This song is sung with hand motions: put a hand to your forehead for each "sea, " twirl a finger around your ear for each "diz," touch your knee for each "knee," and touch the ground on "land." (This version is from Elaine Martin's Kids' Games, and is used by permission.)

chapter 5

SCHOOLYARD

HITS

On Top of a Sandpile
The Halls of Montezuma
No More Pencils
April Fool
Batman Smells
We Three Kings
While Shepherds
Deck the Halls
Just a Boy and a Girl
Miss Polly Had a Dolly
The Barney Song

On Top Of A Sand Pile

On top of a sand pile
All covered with sand
I shot my poor teacher
With a red rubber band.

I shot her with pleasure
I shot her with pride
I could not have missed her
She was forty feet wide!

Sing to the tune of "On Top of Old Smokey."

THE HALLS OF MONTEZUMA

From the halls of Montezuma
To the shores of PTA
We will fight all of our battles
With spitballs and with clay.

We will fight for more recess
And to keep our desks a mess
DIRTY MESS!
We are proud to claim the title
Of teacher's little pests
HEY!

Sing to the tune of "The Marine Hymn."

NO MORE PENCILS

No more pencils
No more books
No more teachers' dirty looks
No more Latin
No more French
No more principal's
Hardwood bench!

April Fool

April Fool has gone apast
And you're the bigger fool at last
Up the ladder and down the tree
You're the bigger fool than me.

Recite this chant when someone plays an April Fool's joke past noon!

Batman

Jingle bells
Batman smells
Robin laid an egg
The Batmobile lost a wheel
The Joker got away
Hey!

Smells

Sing to the tune of "Jingle Bells."

We Three Kings

We three kings of Orient are
Tried to smoke a rubber cigar
It was loaded
And exploded
And scattered us all afar.

Sing to the tune of "We Three Kings."

While Shepherds

While shepherds washed their socks by night
All seated 'round the tub
A shower of Ivory Flakes came down
And they began to scrub.

Sing to the tune of "While Shepherd Watched Their Flocks."

Deck The Halls

Deck the halls with poison ivy

Fa-la-la-la-la, la, la, la, la

Pop a tire and break a window

Fa-la-la-la-la, la, la, la, la.

'Tis the season to be naughty

Fa-la-la-la-la, la, la, la, la

Pop a tire and break a window

Fa-la-la-la-la, la, la, la, la.

Sing to the tune of "Deck the Halls."

Just A Boy and A Girl

Just a boy and a girl in a little canoe
When the moon is shining all around
As they dipped their paddles
They didn't even make a sound.

Well, they talked and they talked
Until the moon went in
And he said, "You better kiss me
Or get out and swim."

So you know what to do
In a little canoe
When the moon is shining all a–
When the moon is shining all a–
When the moon is shining all around
Get out and swim!

Oh, what the heck
Stay in and neck!

But look at him
I'd rather swim!
SPLASH!

Miss Polly
Had A Dolly

Miss Polly had a dolly
Who was sick, sick, sick
So she called for the doctor
To come quick, quick, quick.

The doctor came
With his bag and his hat
And he tapped at the door
With a rat-tat-tat.

He looked at the dolly
And he shook his head
And he said "Miss Polly
Put her straight to bed."

So he wrote on a paper
For a pill, pill, pill
"I'll be back in the morning
With the bill, bill, bill."

Barney Song

I hate you
You hate me
Let's team up and get Barney.
Then a shot rang out
And Barney hit the floor
No more purple dinosaur.

Sing to the tune of "This Old Man."